Preludes & Verses
A Collection for Manuals

Edited by Adrian Vernon Fish

Kevin Mayhew

We hope you enjoy *Preludes and Verses*.
Further copies are available from your local
music shop or Christian bookshop.

In case of difficulty, please contact the publisher direct:

The Sales Department
KEVIN MAYHEW LTD
Rattlesden
Bury St Edmunds
Suffolk IP30 0SZ

Phone 0449 737978
Fax 0449 737834

Please ask for our complete catalogue of outstanding Church Music.

Front Cover: *Ikon of the Virgin*, Smolenskaja Monastery, Moscow, 16th century.
Kremlin Museums, Moscow / Bridgeman Art Library, London.
Reproduced by permission.

Cover Design: Juliette Clarke and Graham Johnstone.
Picture Research: Jane Rayson.
Music Setting: Tricia Oliver.

First published in Great Britain in 1992 by
KEVIN MAYHEW LTD
Rattlesden, Bury St Edmunds, Suffolk IP30 OSZ

© Copyright 1992 Kevin Mayhew Ltd.

ISBN 0 86209 331 7

Printed and bound in Great Britain.

Contents

Foreword

I have given this collection the title *Preludes and Verses* because it neatly encapsulates the two traditions represented.

The term 'Chorale Prelude', or, more popularly, 'Prelude', generally refers to the hymn tunes of the Protestant tradition so luminously crafted by the likes of Buxtehude and Bach and their contemporaries.

The more Catholic plainsong tradition is generally termed 'Verses' or 'Versets'.

In *Preludes and Verses* we begin in sixteenth century England and Holland and travel by way of France to Denmark and Germany.

ADRIAN VERNON FISH

ADRIAN VERNON FISH is a composer, organist and harpsichordist. He studied at the Royal College of Music in London under Herbert Howells, Alan Ridout, Nicholas Danby, Joseph Horovitz and Ruth Dyson.

He composes in most forms, from symphonies to cabaret songs.

THOU WHO ART THREE IN ONE

Jan Pieterszoon Sweelinck (1562 - 1621)

molto rall.

CHRIST, OUR LORD, TO JORDAN CAME

Johann Sebastian Bach (1685 - 1750)

9

MY DEAR GOD

Dietrich Buxtehude (1637 - 1707)

O GOD, THY SOLDIERS' CROWN AND GUARD

Girolamo Cavazzoni (c.1525 - c.1577)

LAMB OF GOD

François Couperin (1668 - 1733)

HONOUR BE TO GOD ON HIGH

Johann Sebastian Bach (1685 - 1750)

rall.

19

JESUS CHRIST, OUR REDEEMER

Dietrich Buxtehude (1637 - 1707)

NOW REJOICE, CHRISTIANS TOGETHER

Johann Ernst Rembt (1749 - 1810)

allargando

DEAREST JESU, WE ARE HERE

Johann Rinck (1770 - 1846)

NOW PRAISE THE LORD

Dietrich Buxtehude (1637 - 1707)

OUR FATHER IN HEAVEN

Samuel Scheidt (1587 - 1654)

NOW ALL THE WOODS ARE CALM

Johann Sebastian Bach (1685 - 1750)

WHERE ONLY THE LORD GIVES GUIDANCE

Niels Gade (1817 - 1890)

O CHRIST, WHO ART THE LIGHT AND DAY

16th century English

ALL MEN MUST DIE

A. Reinhard (1831 - 1912)

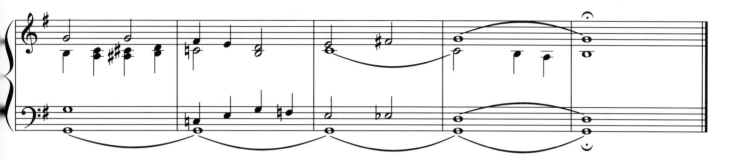

GOD OF HEAVEN AND EARTH

Adolf Hesse (1809 - 1863)

ONLY TO YOU, LORD JESUS CHRIST

Jan Pieterszoon Sweelinck (1562 - 1621)

DEEPLY I YEARN

C. Karow (1790 - 1863)

WHO LETS THE DEAR GOD PRESIDE

A. Kehrer (1811 - 1850)

SING MY TONGUE

Jean Titelouze (1563 - 1633)

44

REJOICE GREATLY, O MY SOUL

A. Reinhard (1831 - 1912)

CHRIST, REDEEMER OF ALL

John Redford (d. 1547)

PRAISE TO THE LORD

Johann Rinck (1770 - 1846)

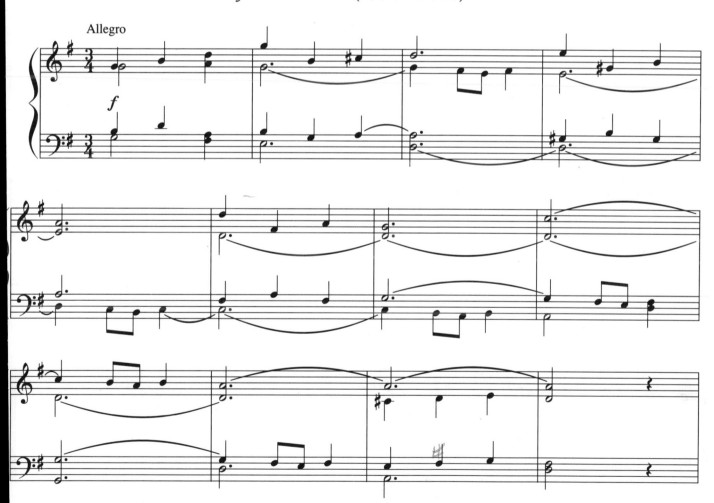